Reasoning and Writing

Level A
Workbook 2

Siegfried Engelmann

Karen Lou Seitz Davis

SRA

A Division of The McGraw-Hill Companies

Columbus, Ohio

Cover Credits

(tl, tr) PhotoDisc, (bl) Comstock.

SRA/McGraw-Hill

A Division of The McGraw·Hill Companies

Copyright © 2001 by SRA/McGraw-Hill.

Send all inquiries to:
SRA/McGraw-Hill
4400 Easton Commons
Columbus, OH 43219

Printed in the United States of America.

ISBN 0-02-684751-5

9 10 11 12 13 DBH 13 12 11 10 09 08

Lesson 36

A.

1. true false   3. true false
2. true false   4. true false

B.

1

2

C.

1. MARKET
2.
3.
4.
5.
6.

D.

1.

2.

3.

4.

Lesson 37

A.

1.

2.

3.

4.

B.

1. true   false
2. true   false
3. true   false

C.

D.

Lesson 38

A.

□ □ □

□ □ □

B.

1. true   false
2. true   false
3. true   false
4. true   false
5. true   false

C.

Lesson 39

A.

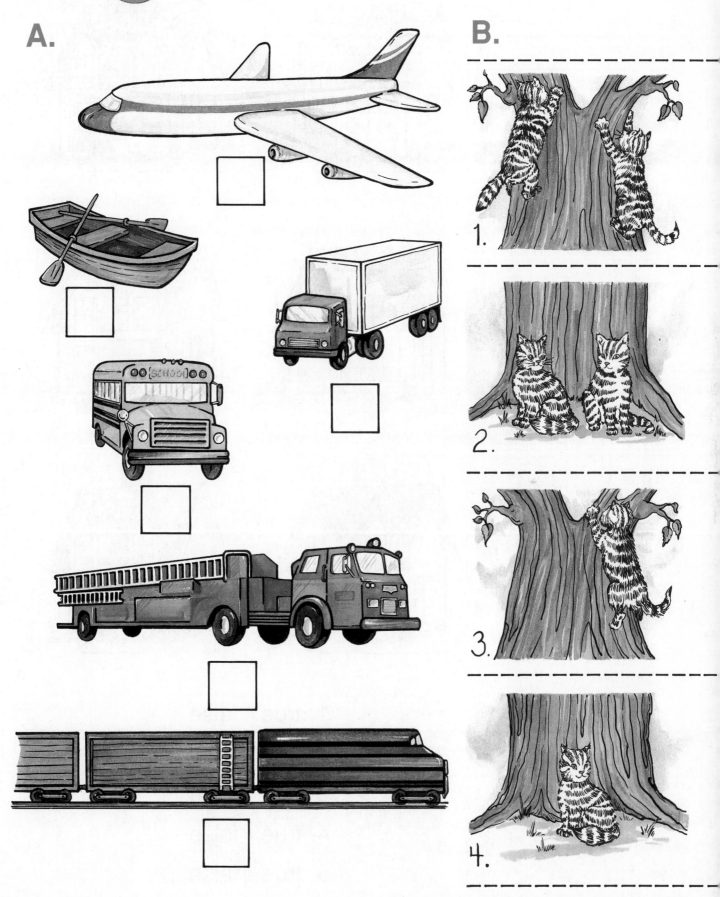

B.

1.

2.

3.

4.

C.

1. true   false

2. true   false

3. true   false

4. true   false

5. true   false

D.

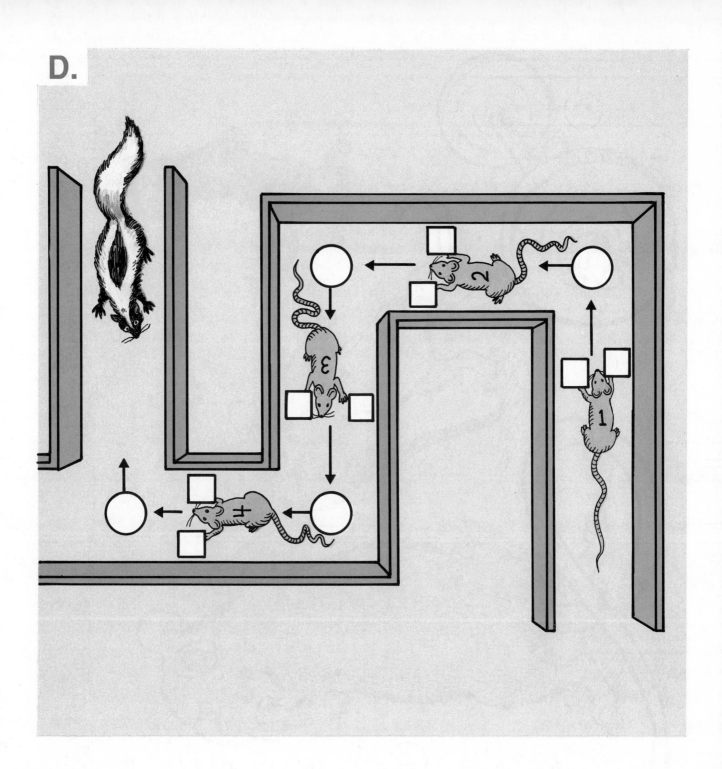

A.

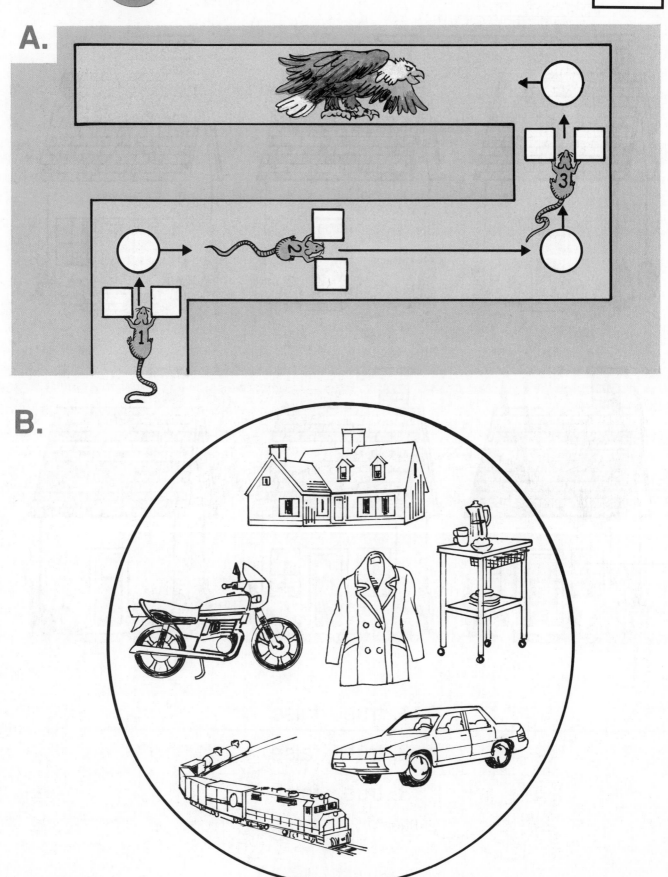

B.

C.

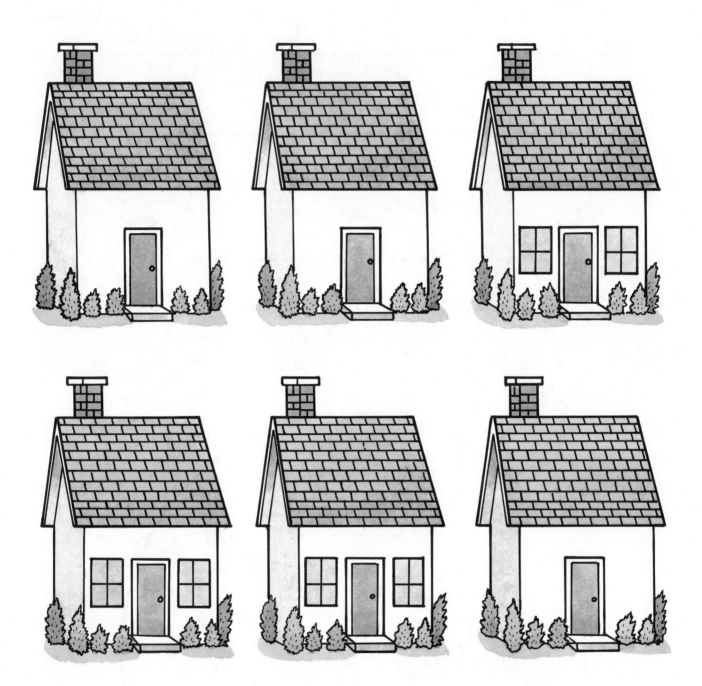

1. true   false

2. true   false

3. true   false

4. true   false

Lesson 41

A.

B.

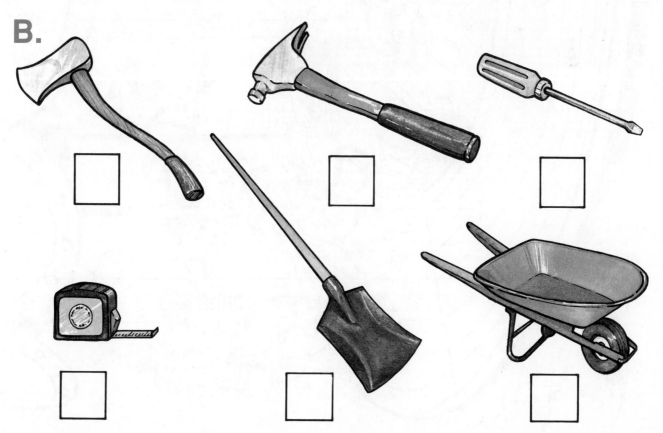

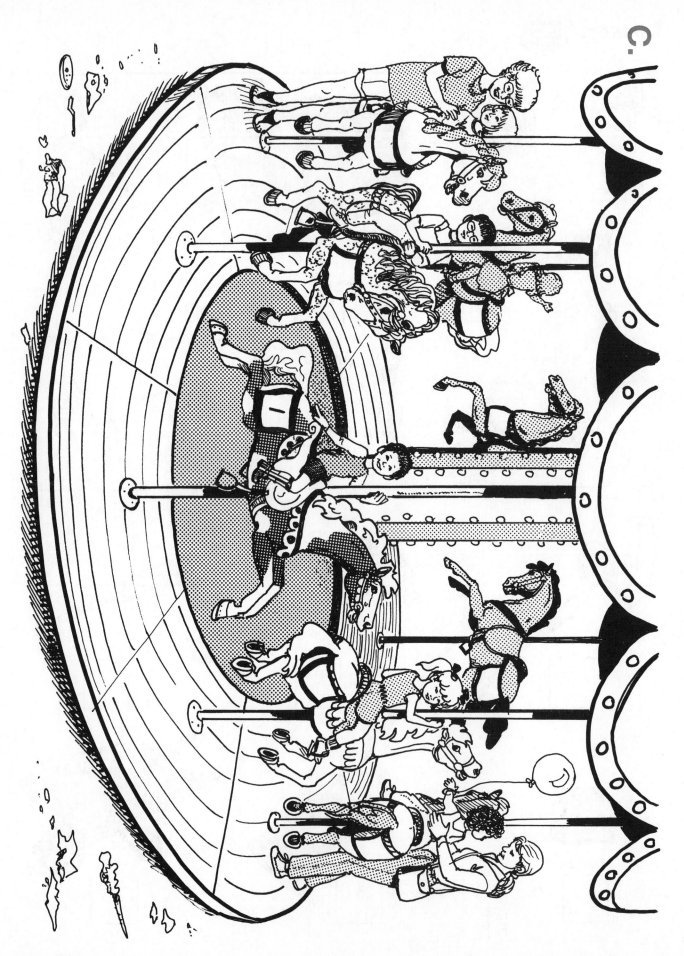

Lesson 42

A.

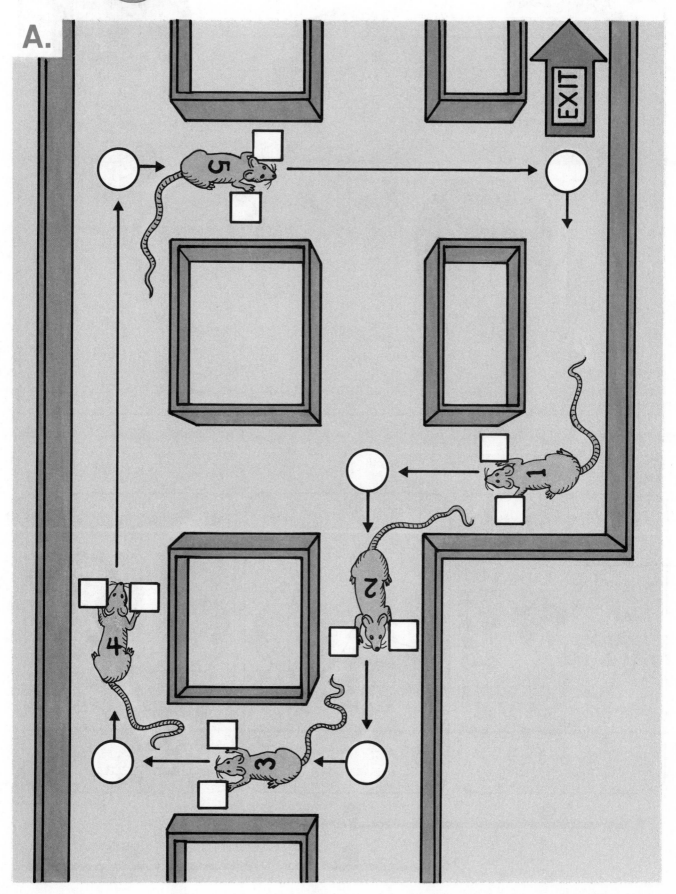

C.

D.

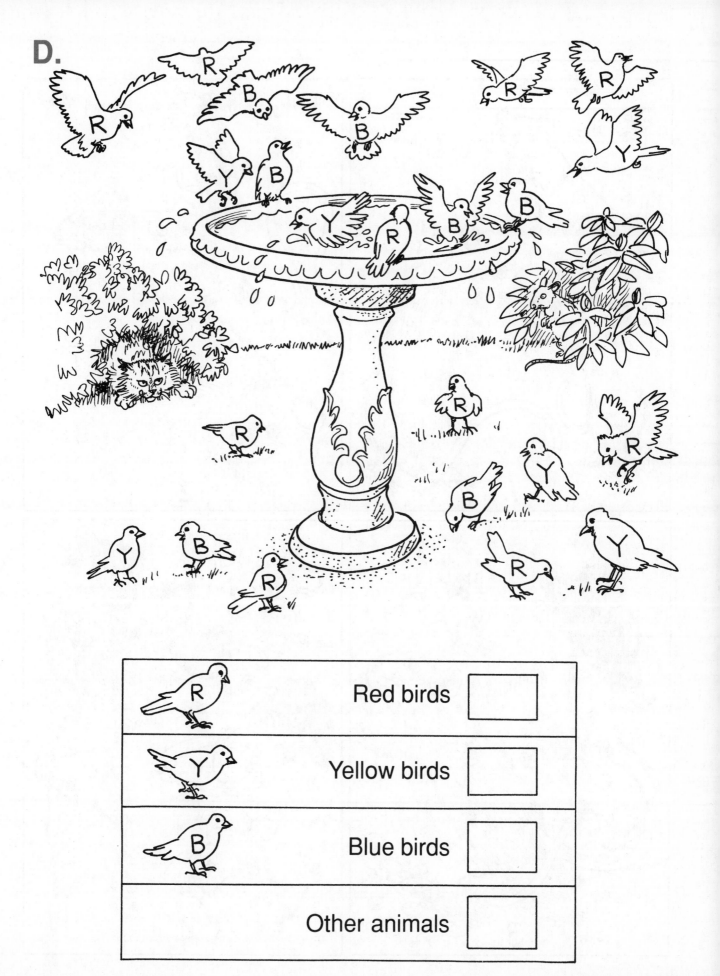

	Red birds	
	Yellow birds	
	Blue birds	
	Other animals	

E.

1.

2.

3.

4.

Lesson 43

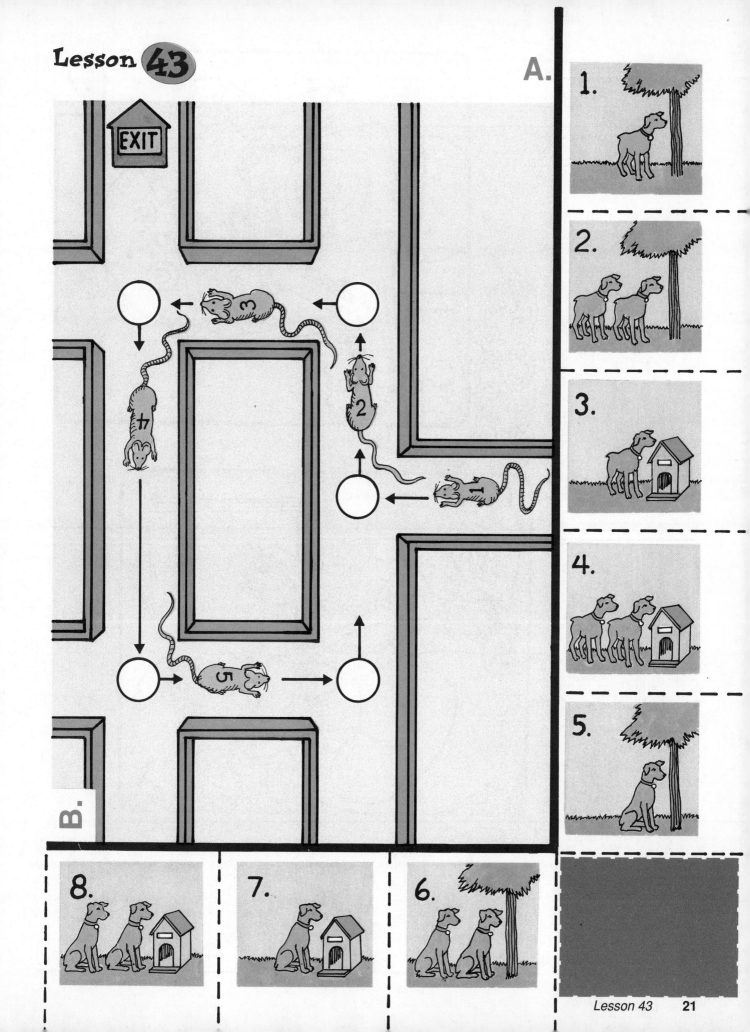

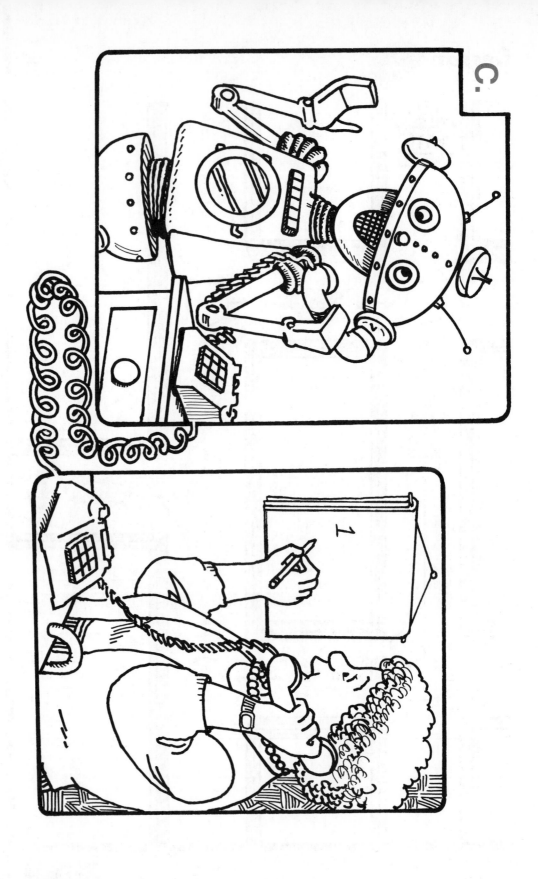

Lesson 44

A.

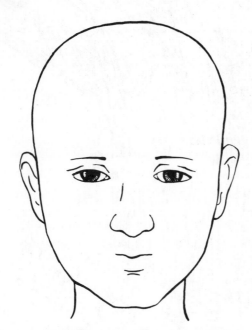

1. true   false

2. true   false

3. true   false

4. true   false

B.

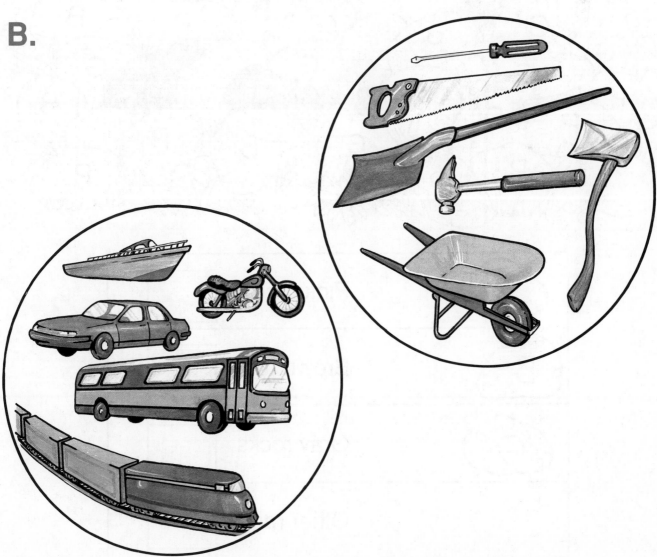

C.

P	Pink rocks	
B	Brown rocks	
G	Gray rocks	
	Other rocks	

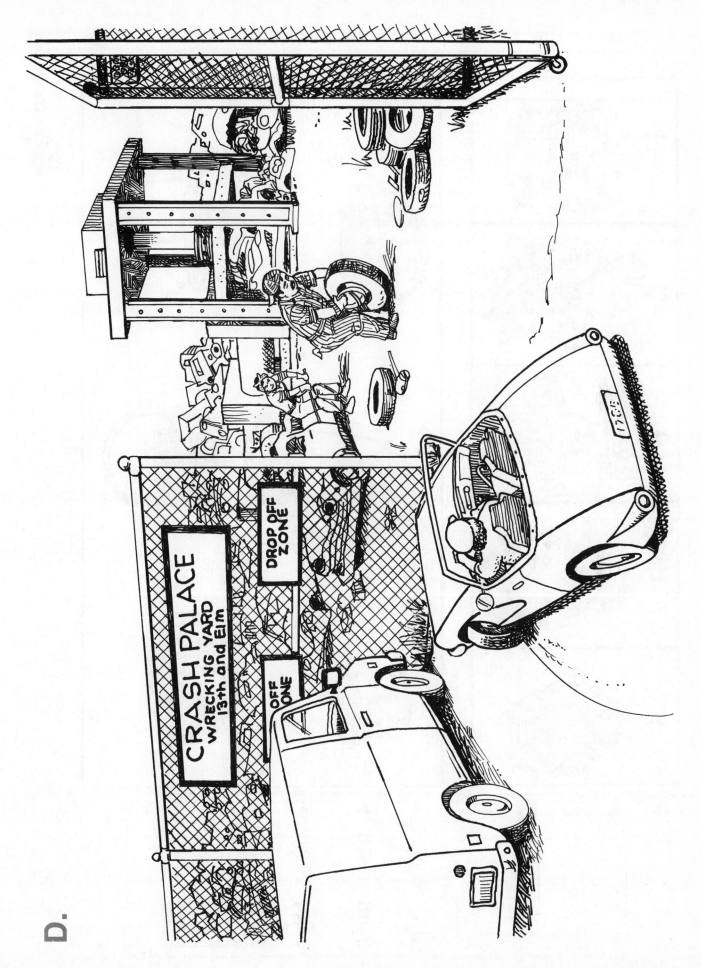

D.

A.

1. true   false

2. true   false

3. true   false

4. true   false

B.

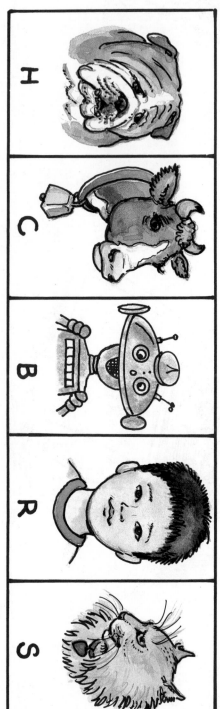

| H | C | B | R | S |

1. _____

2. _____

3. _____

4. _____

5. _____

C.

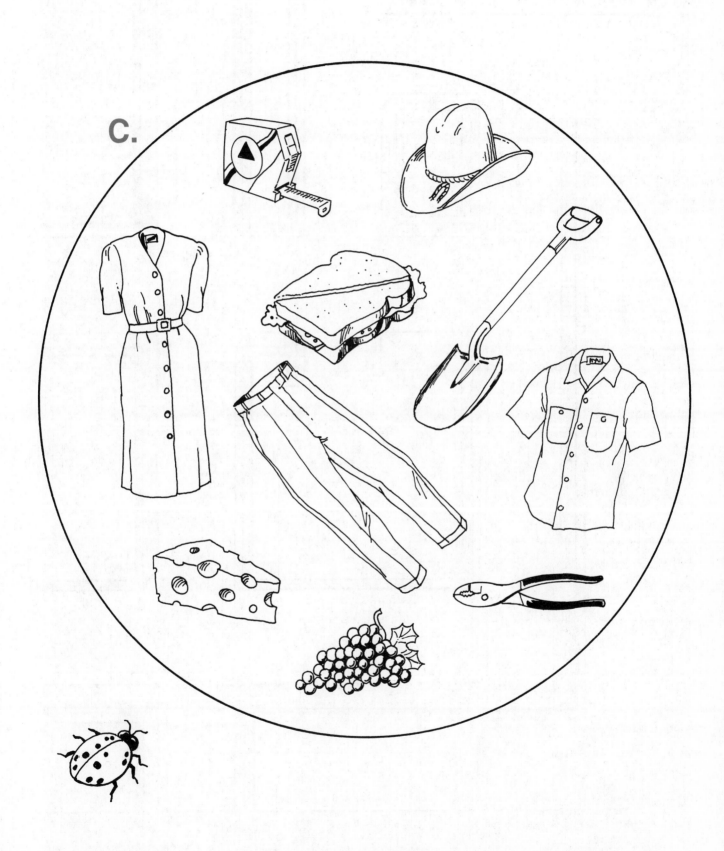

Lesson 46

A.

B.

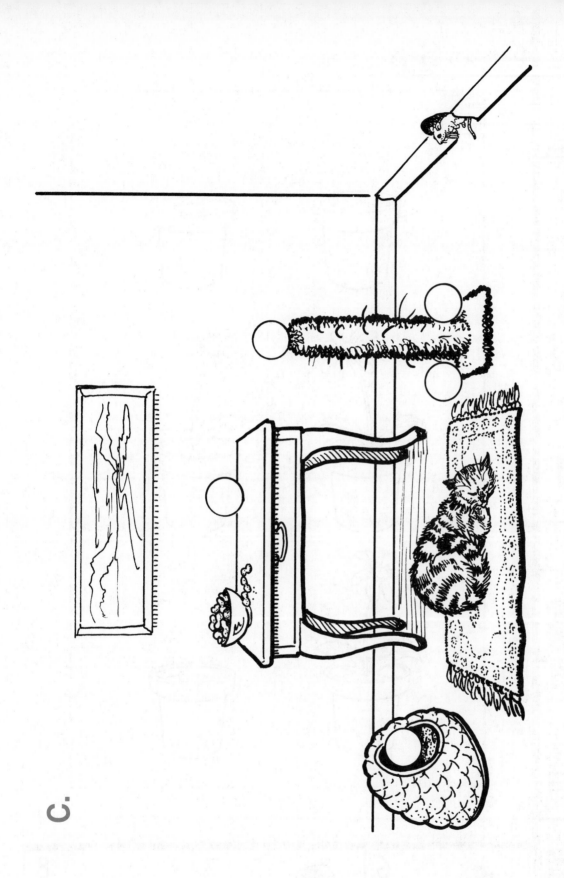

C.

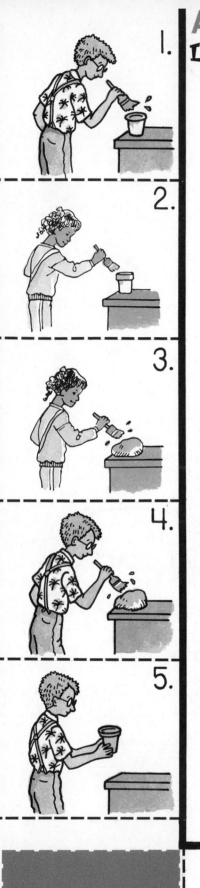

B.

6.

7.

8.

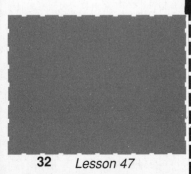

C.

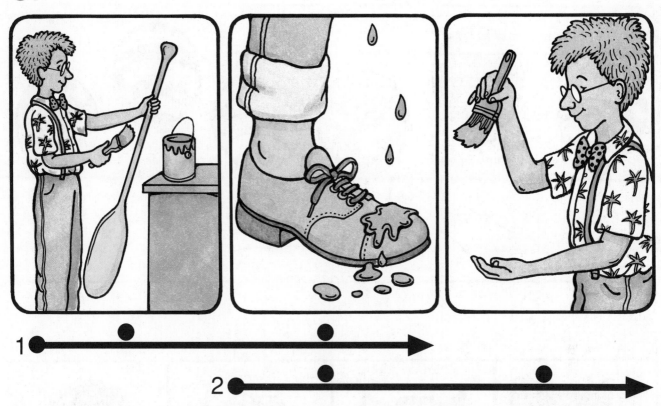

D.

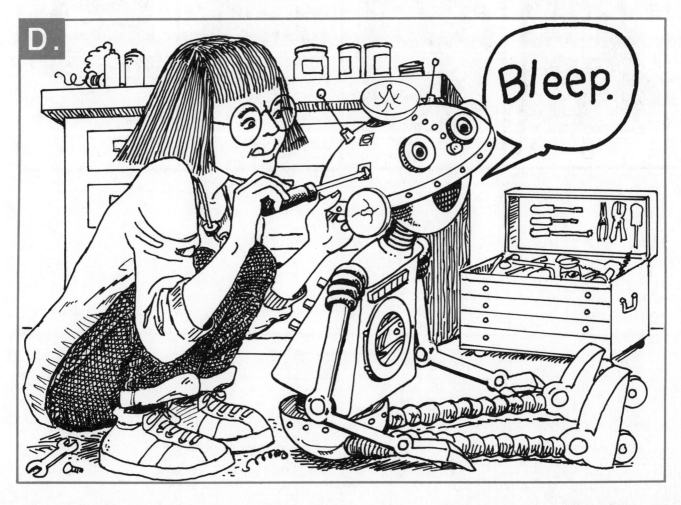

Lesson

A.

B.

B   S   R   M

1. _____

2. _____

3. _____

4. _____

5. _____

C.

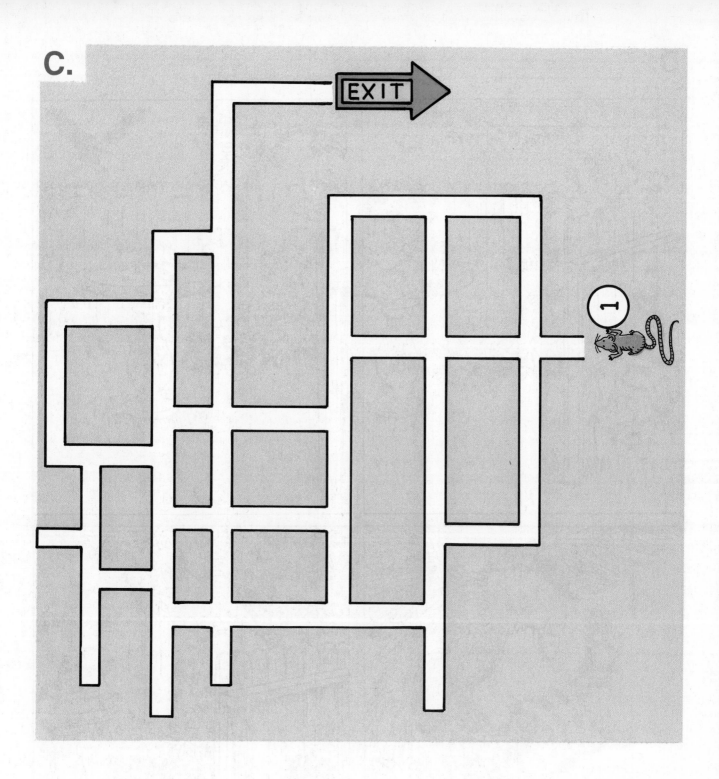

1.

2.

3.

4.

Lesson 49

A.

B.

C.

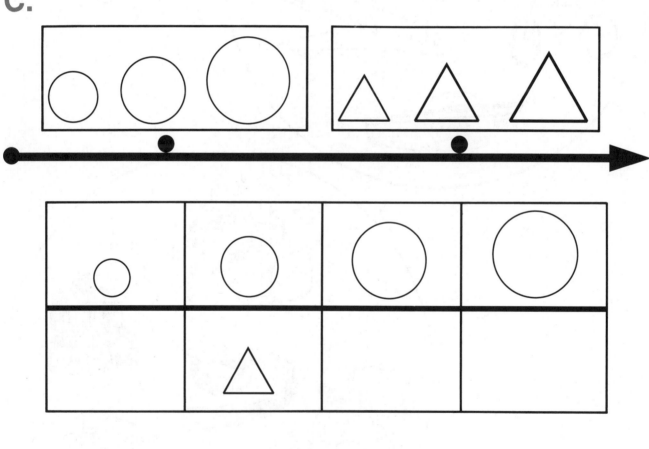

D.

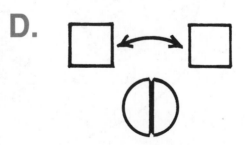

E.

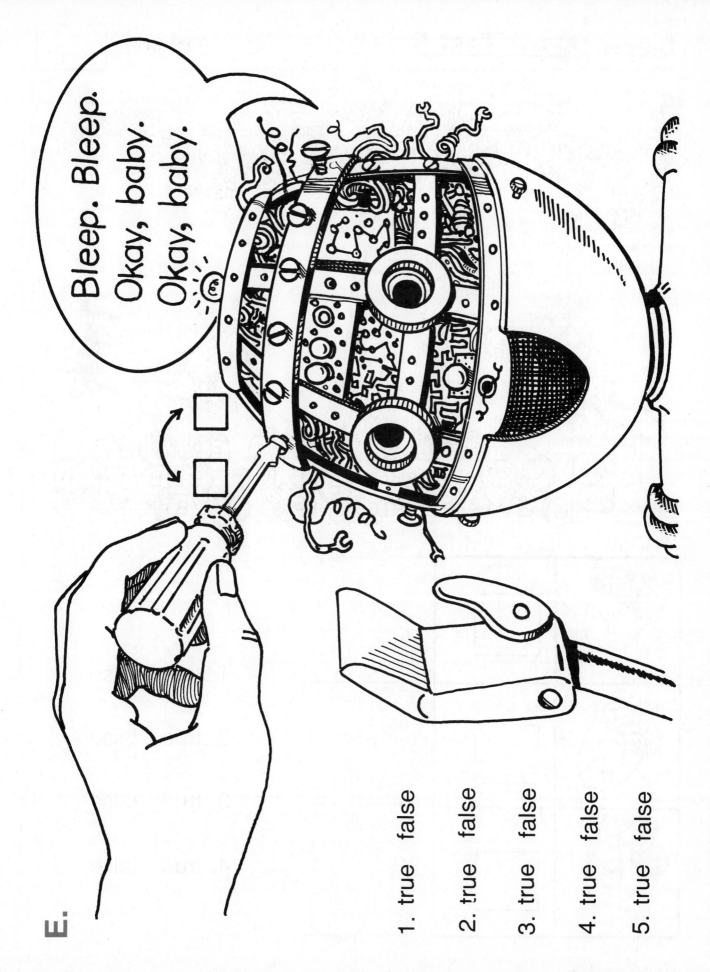

1. true false

2. true false

3. true false

4. true false

5. true false

A.

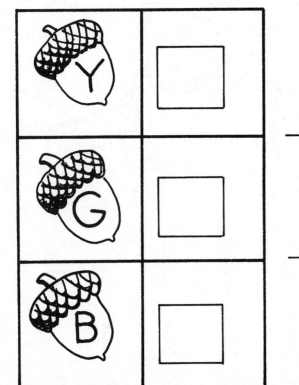

1. true   false

2. true   false

3. true   false

4. true   false

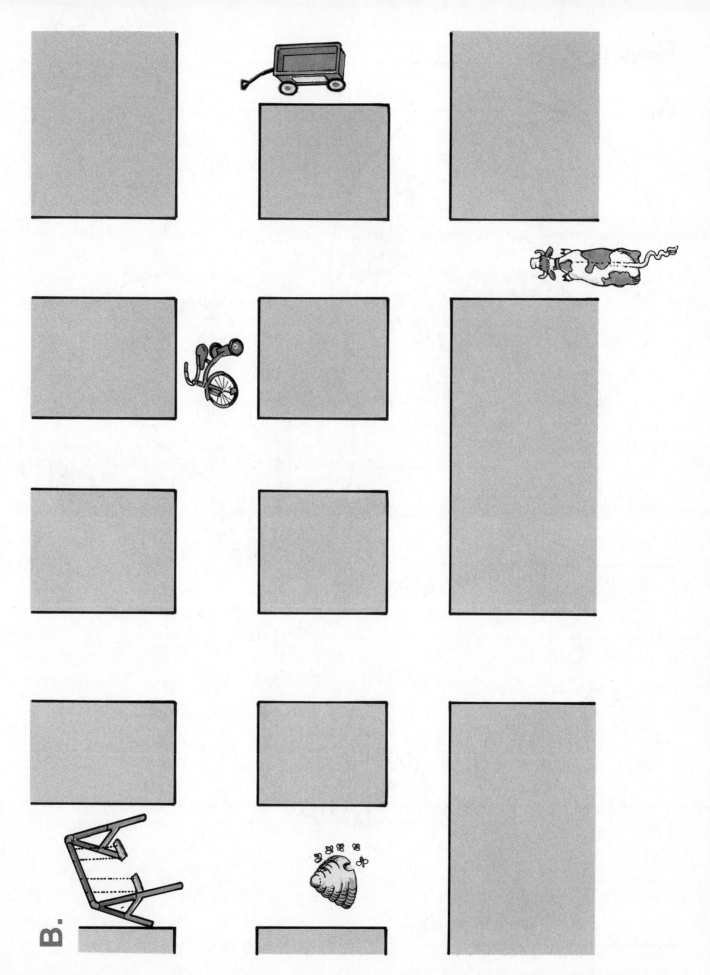

Lesson 51

A.

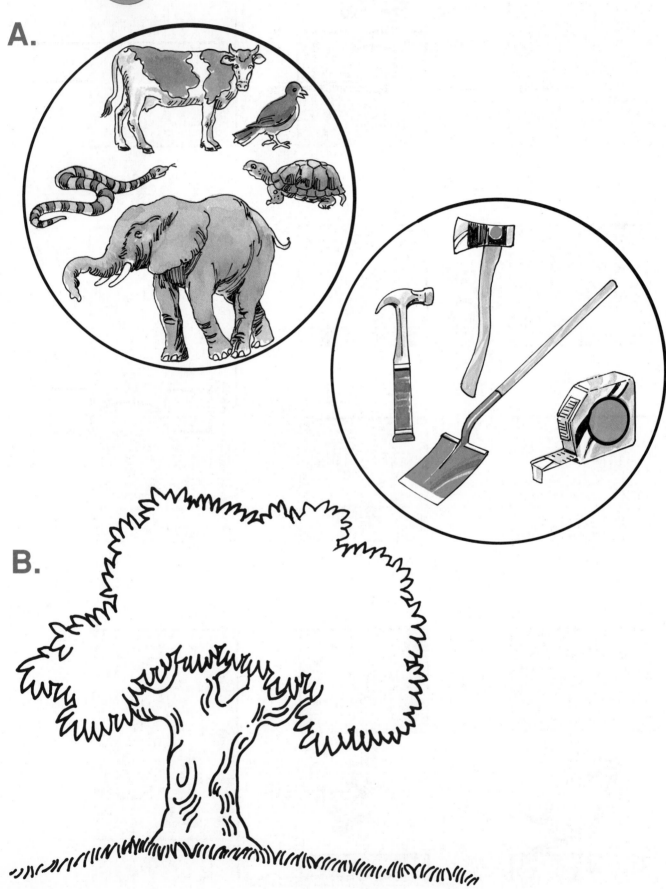

B.

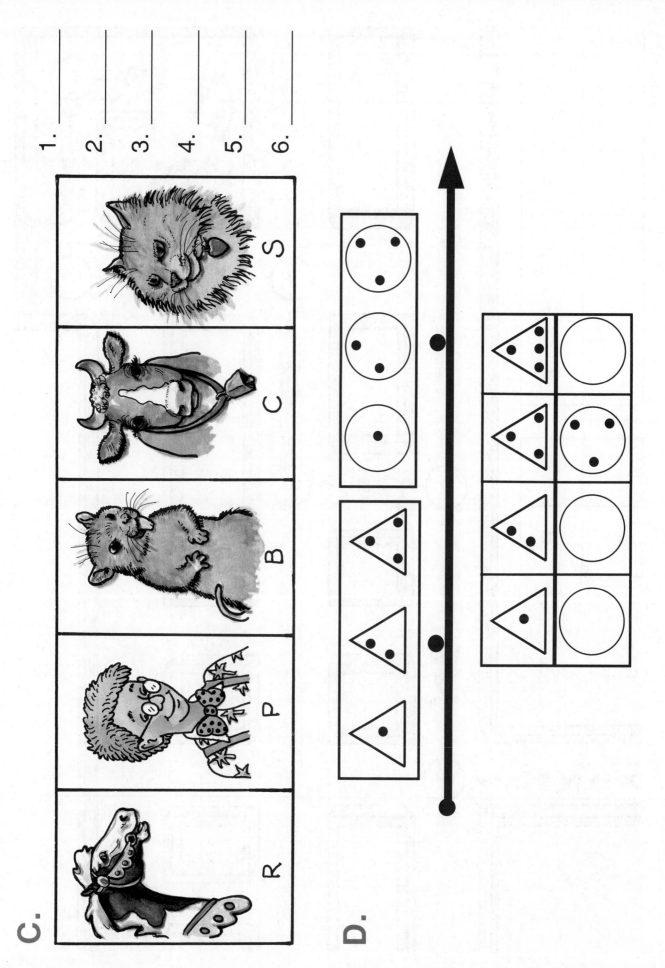

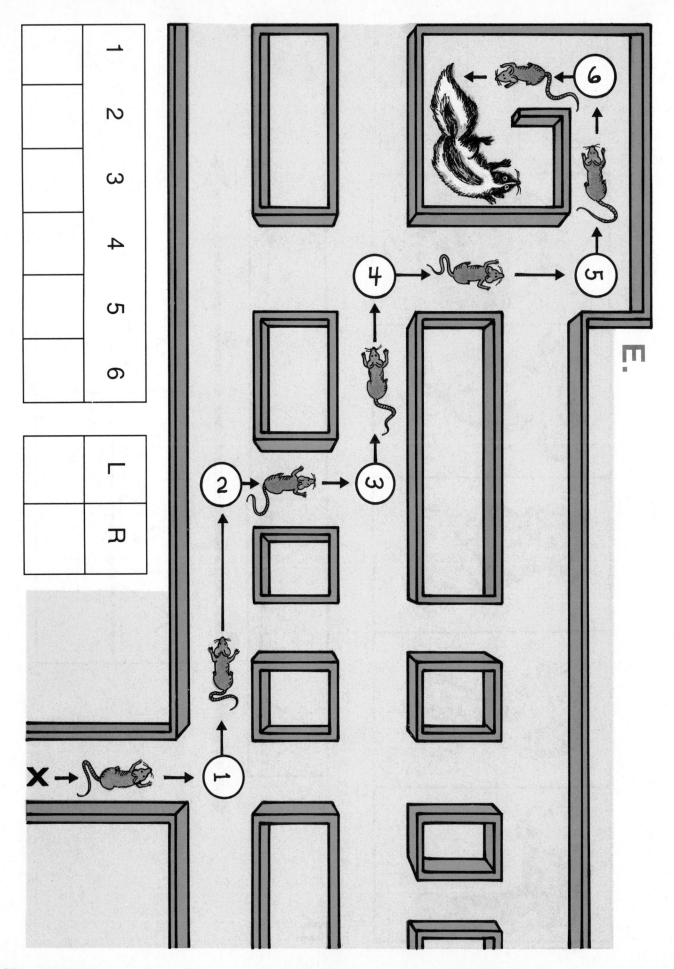

E.

Lesson 52

A.

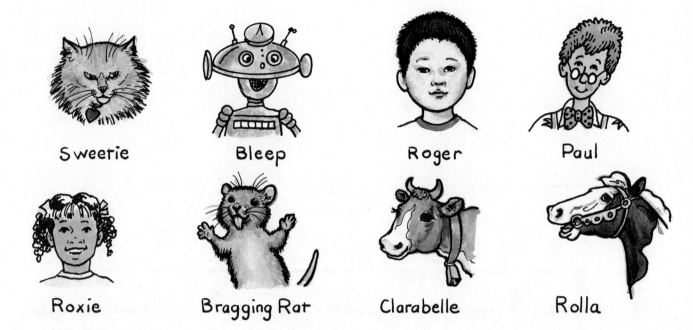

Sweetie   Bleep   Roger   Paul

Roxie   Bragging Rat   Clarabelle   Rolla

B.

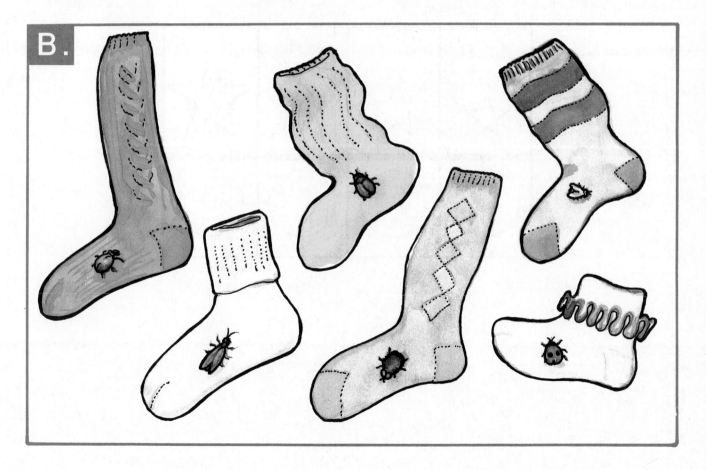

C.

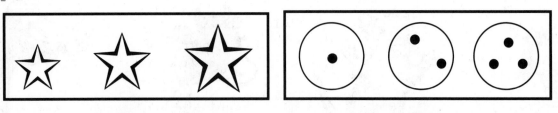

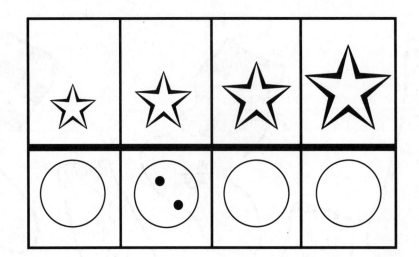

D.

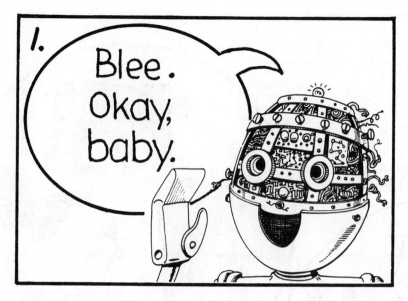
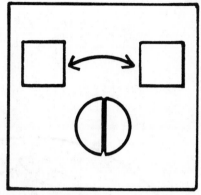

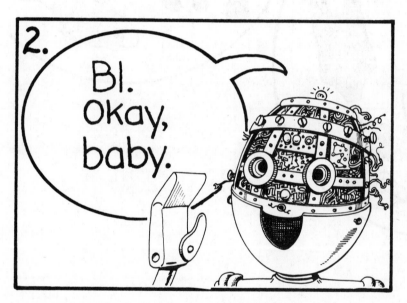
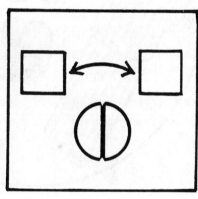

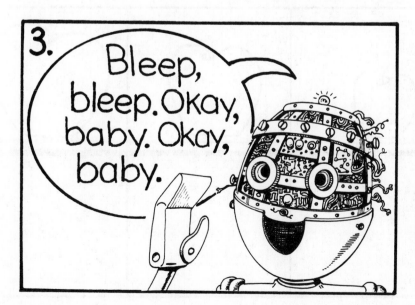
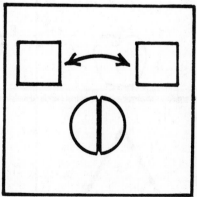

A.

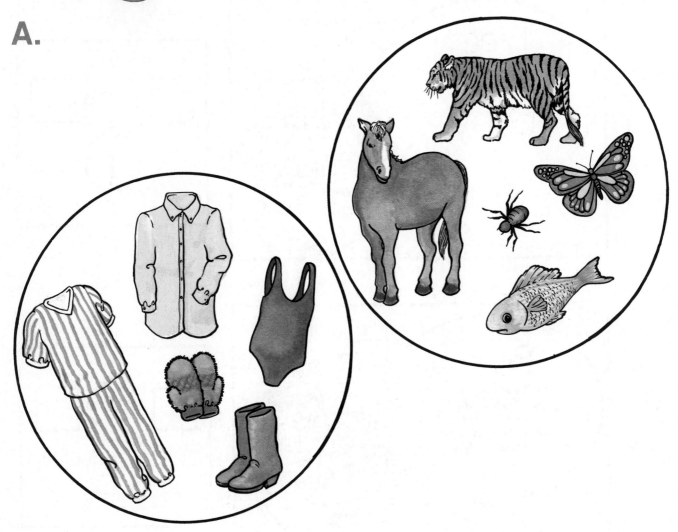

B.

C.

1. true   false

2. true   false

3. true   false

4. true   false

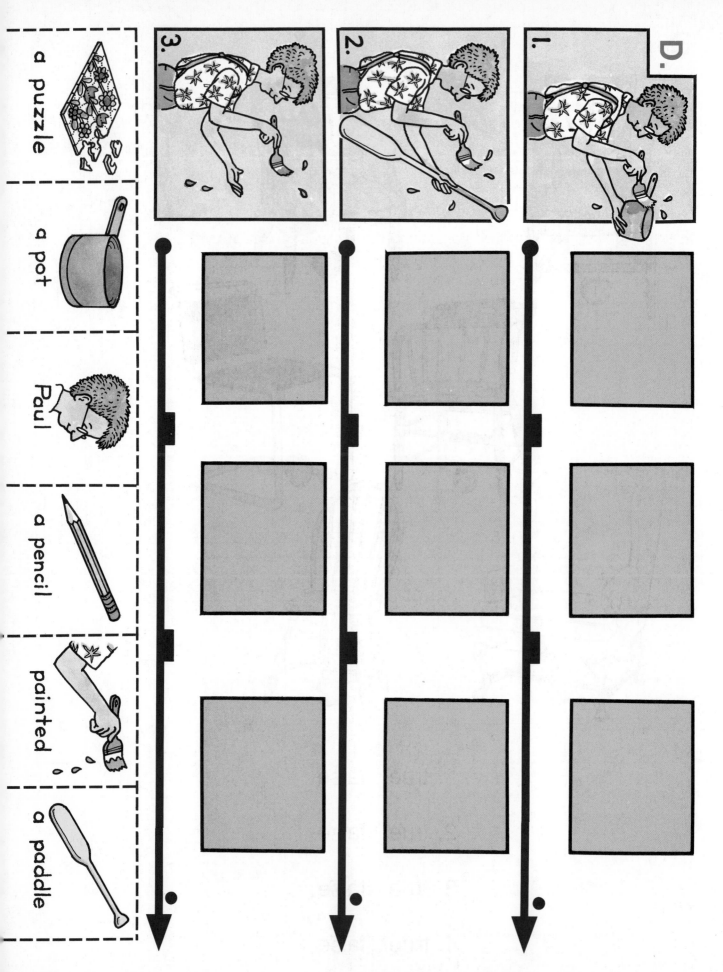

Lesson 54

A.

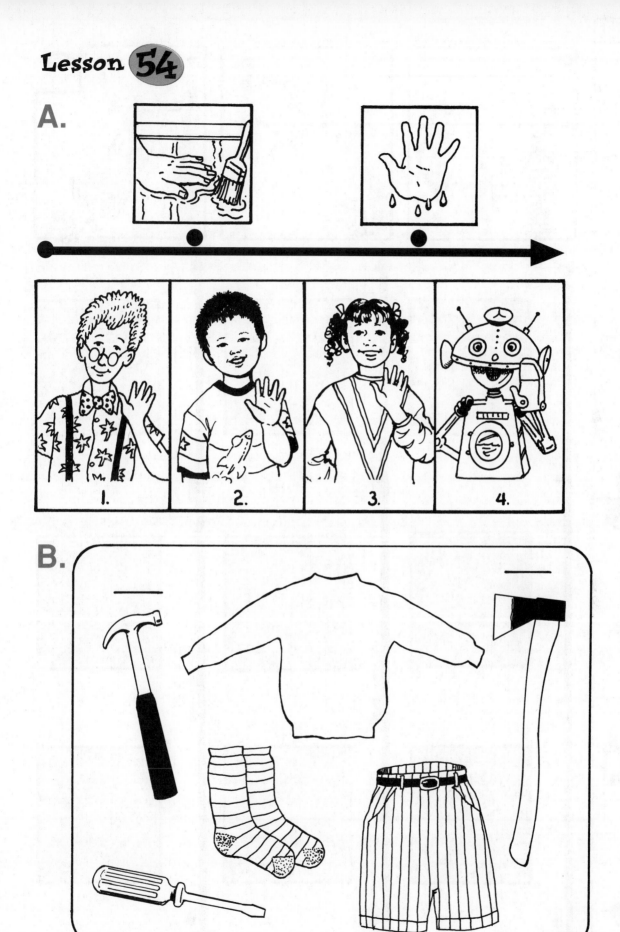

1.   2.   3.   4.

B.

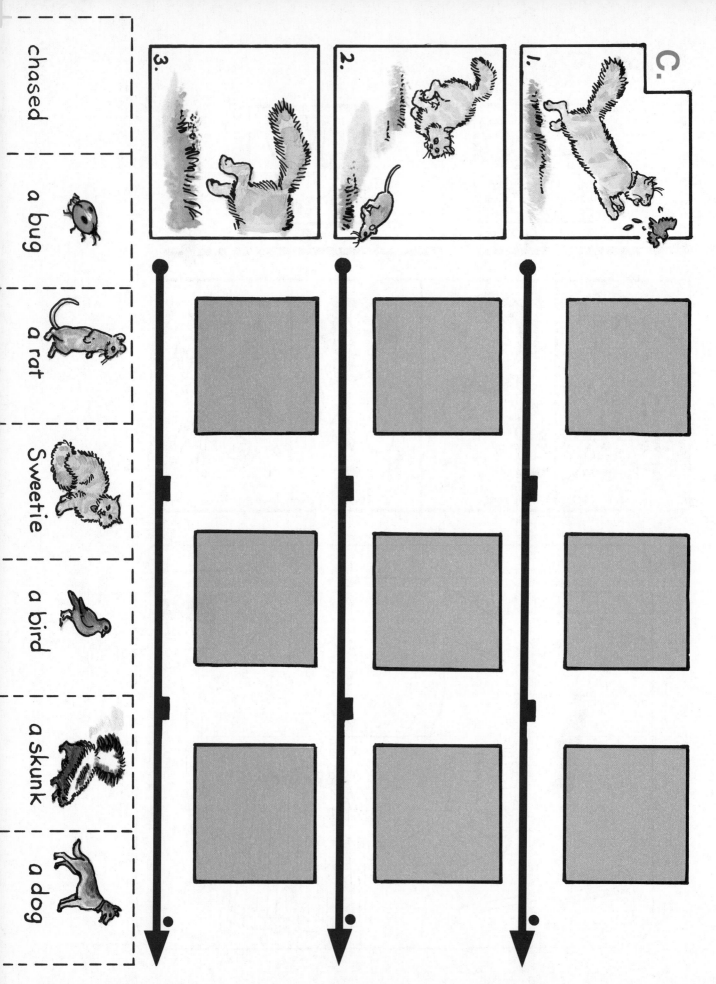

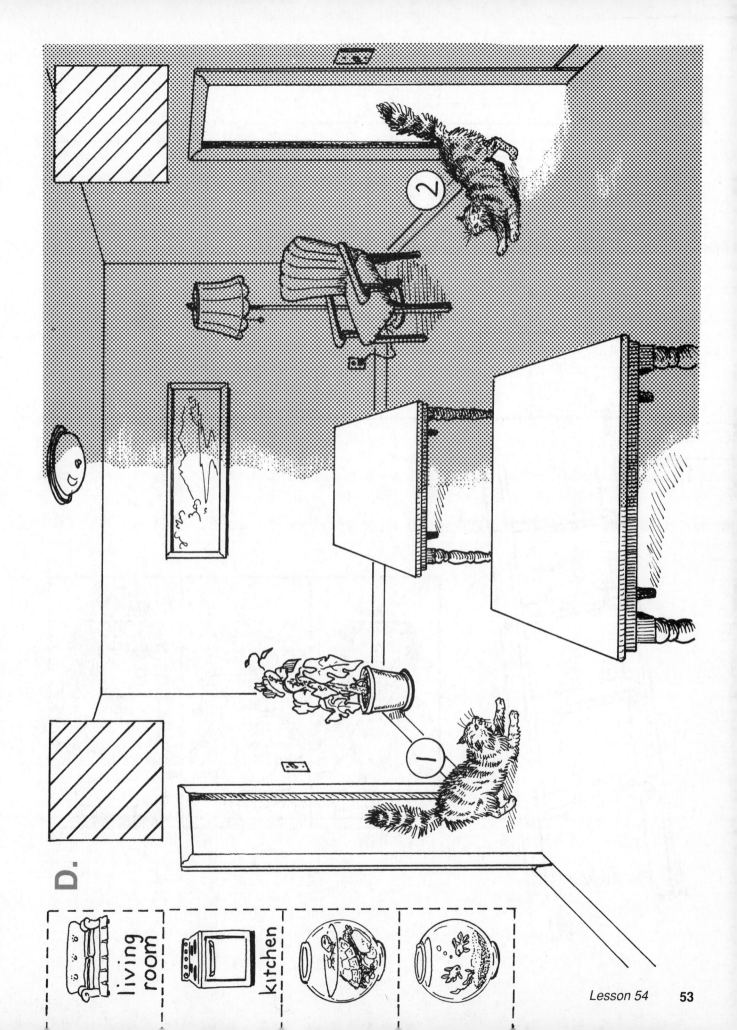

D.

living room

kitchen

Lesson 55

A.

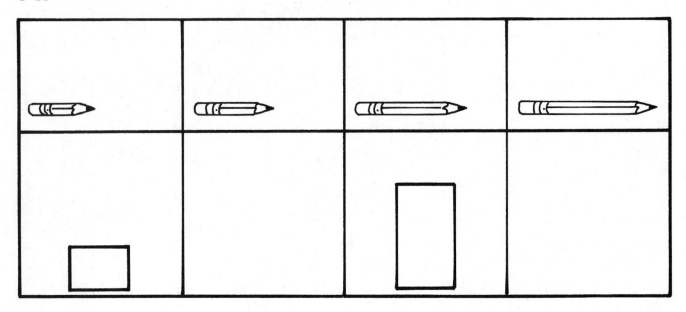

B.

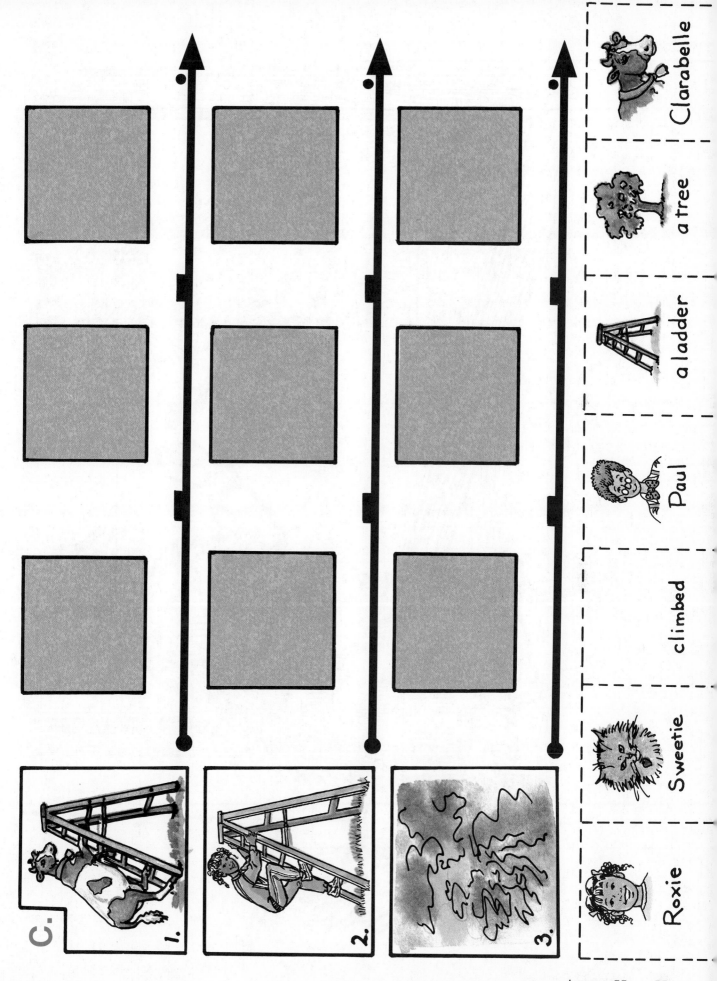

B.

1.

Okay, baby

2.

Okay baby.

3.

4.

5.

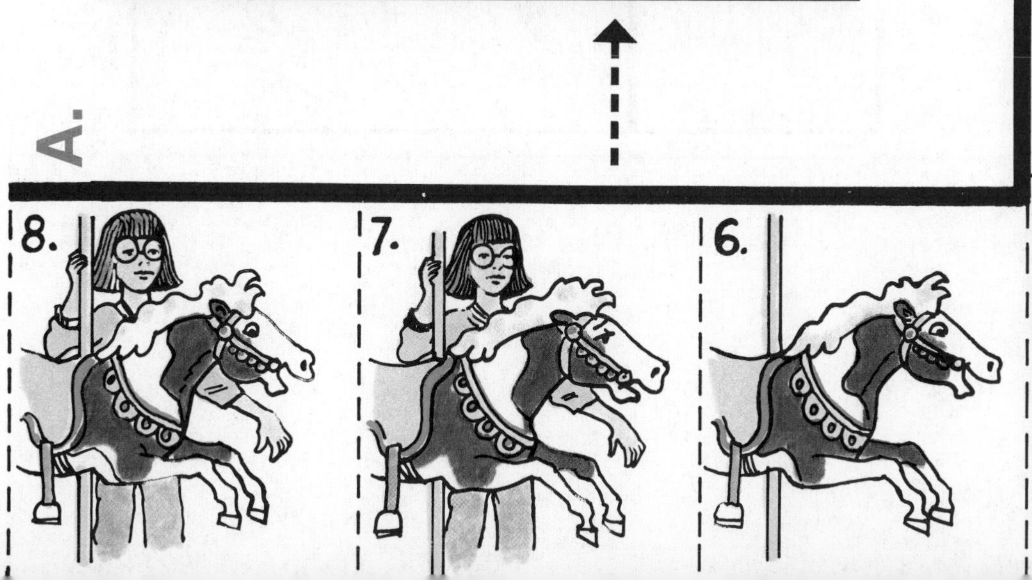

A.

8.

7.

6.

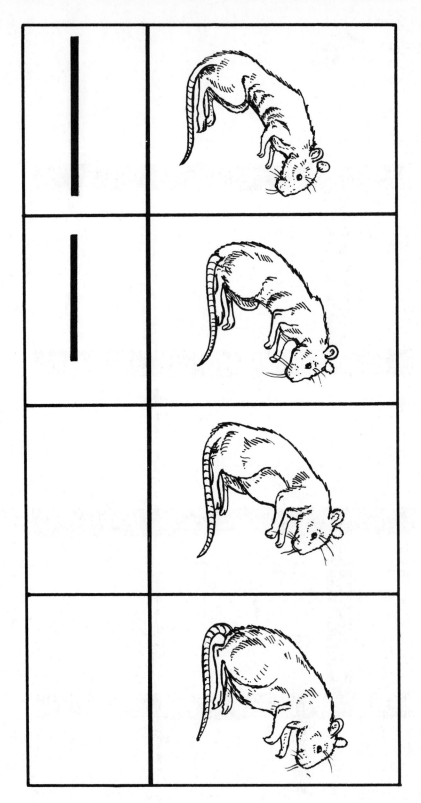

D.

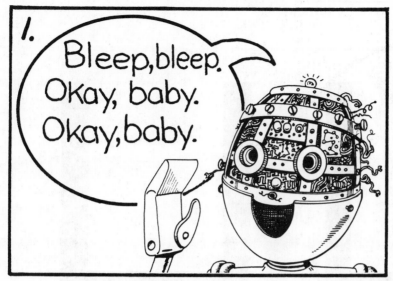 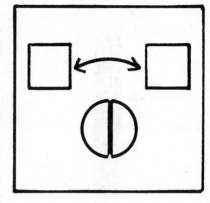

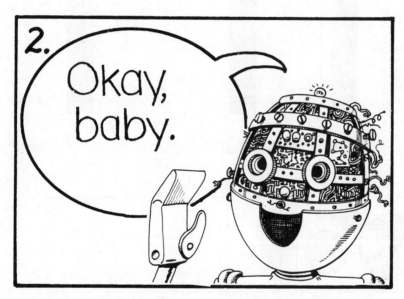 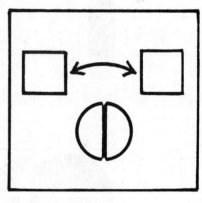

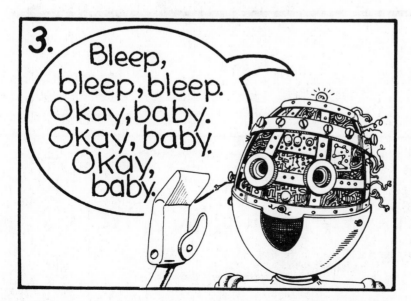 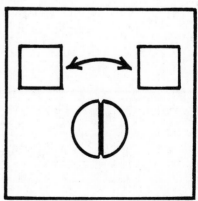

A.

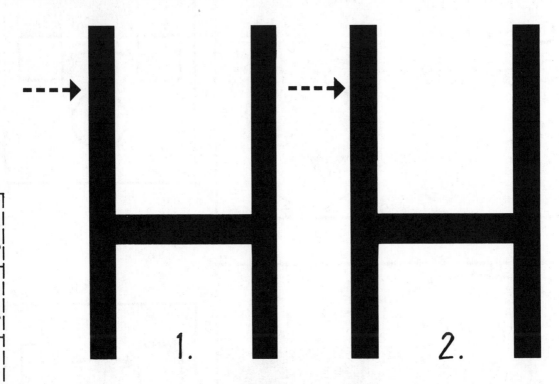

1.

2.

B.

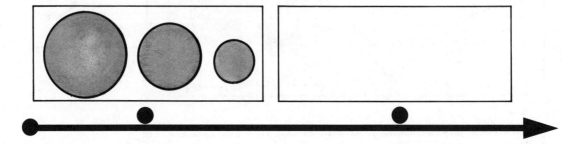

C.

A.

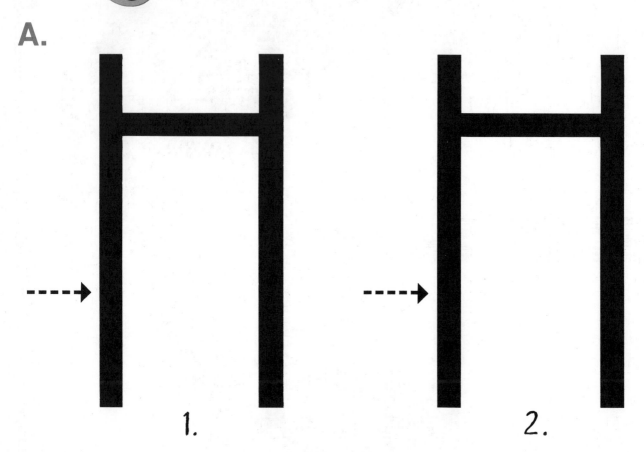

1.

2.

B.

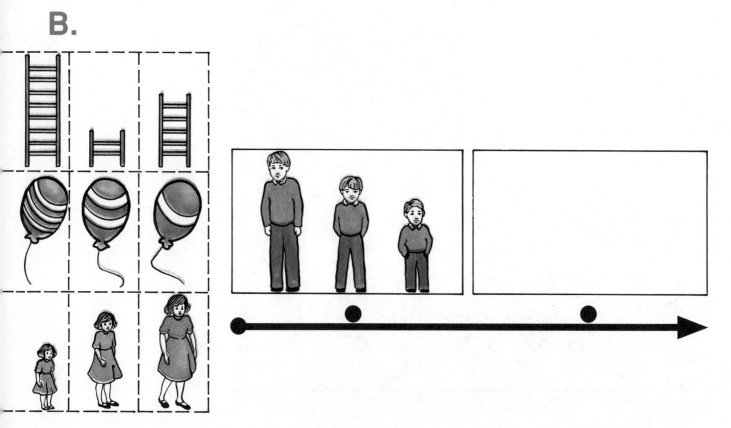

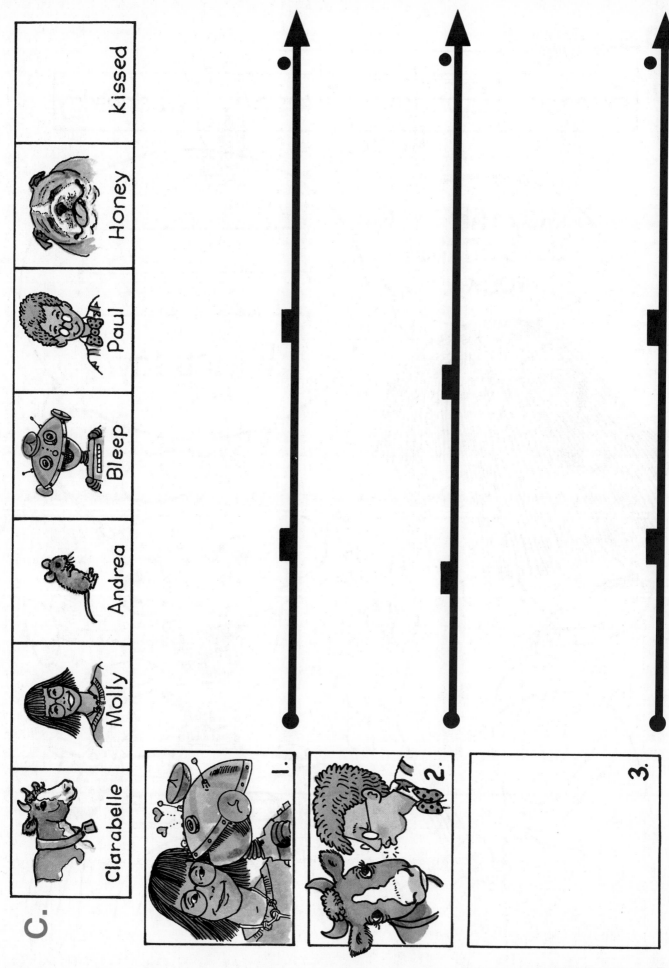

D.

Sunday	Monday	Tuesday	Wednesday

Lesson 59

A.

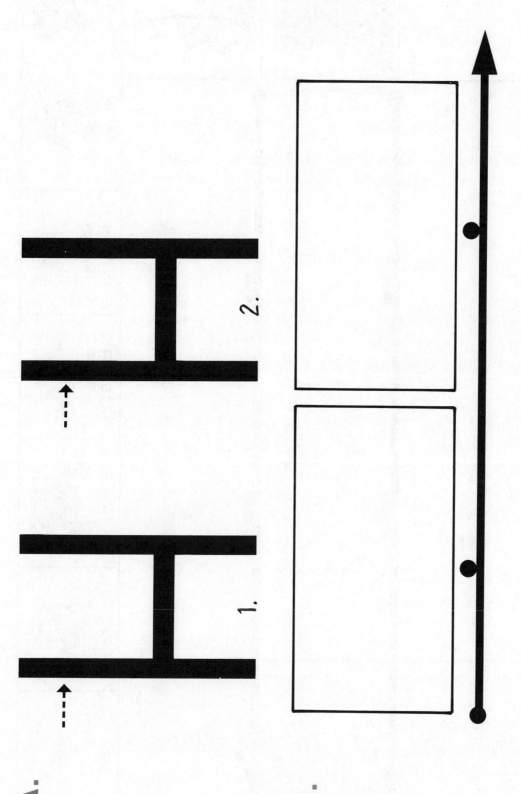

1.   2.

B.

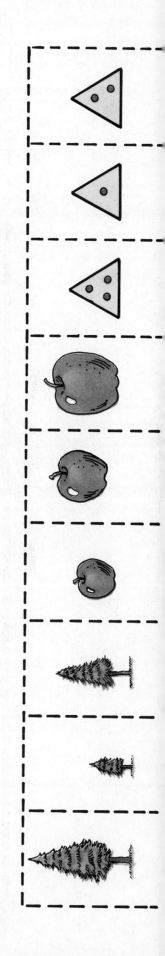

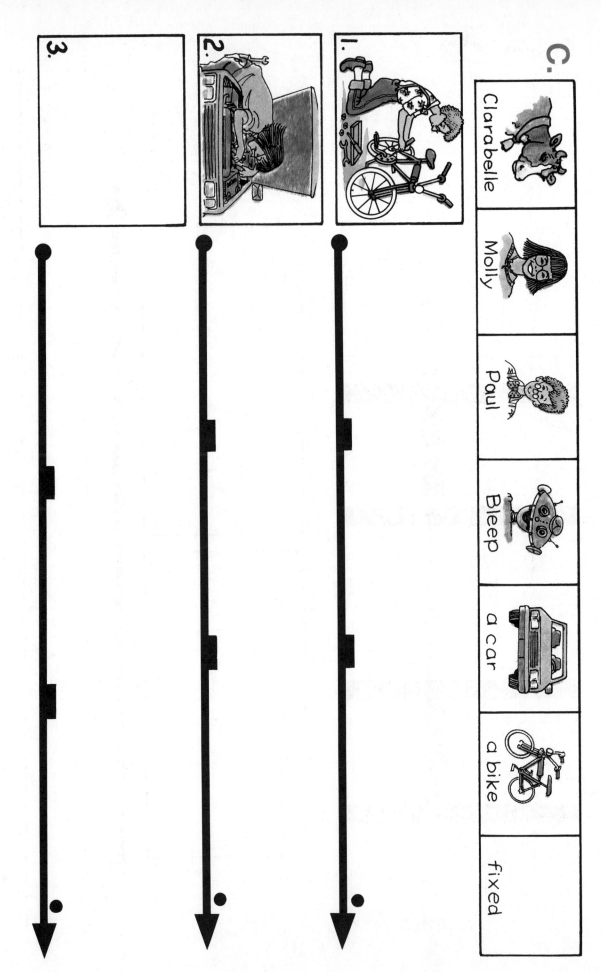

D.

Wednesday	Thursday	Friday	Saturday

Wow, you can say ALL the days of the week!

Sunday,
Monday,
Tuesday,

_____,

_____,

_____,

_____.

Test Score

A.

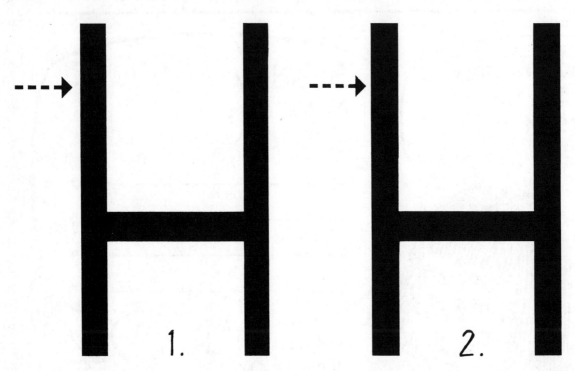

1.

2.

B.

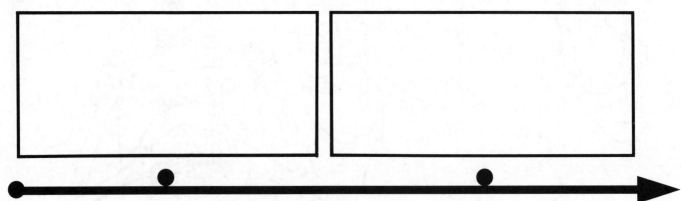

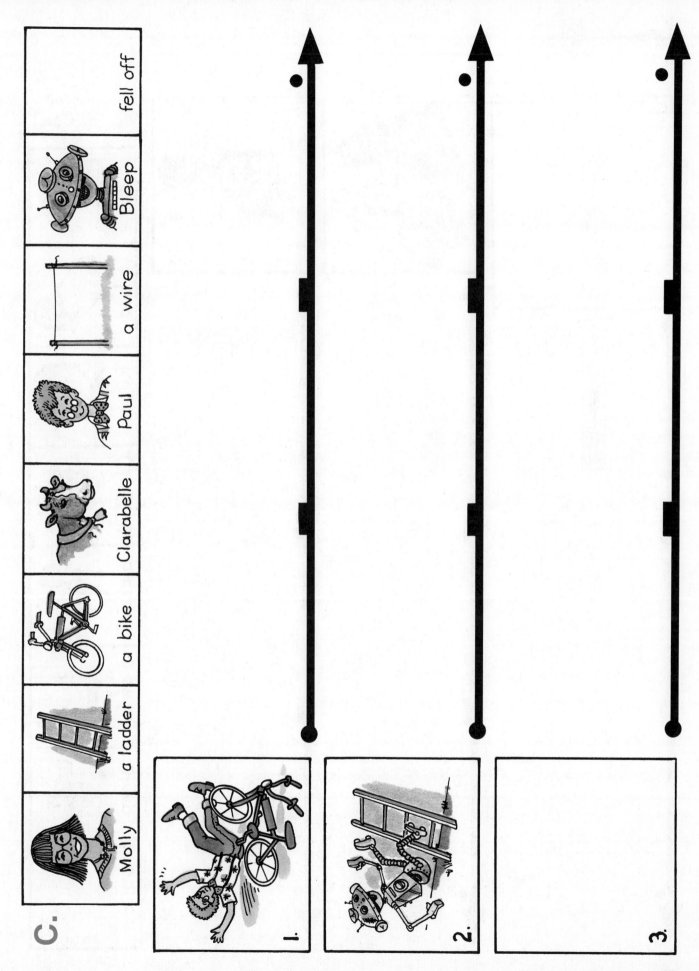

Lesson 61

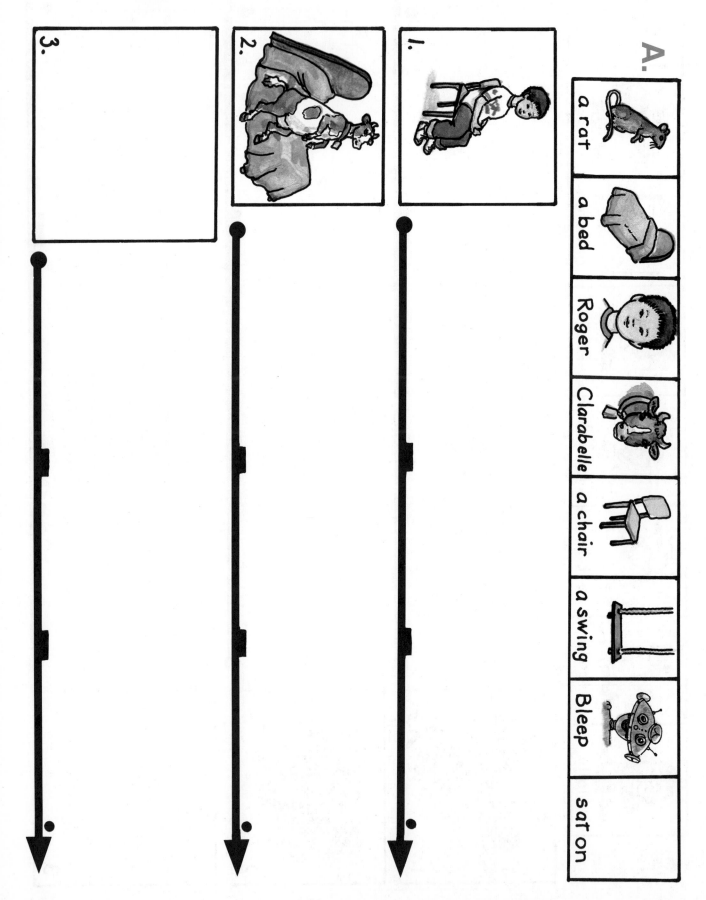

A.

a rat | a bed | Roger | Clarabelle | a chair | a swing | Bleep | sat on

3.

2.

1.

B.

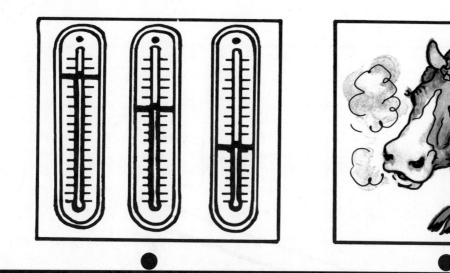

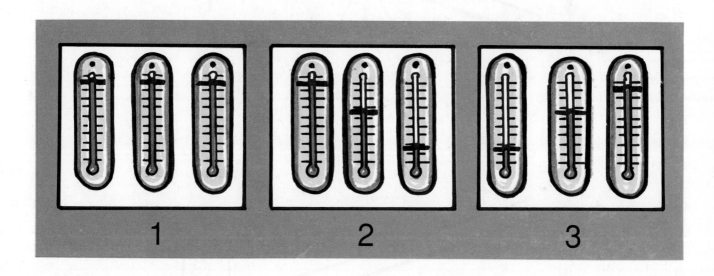

1   2   3

C.

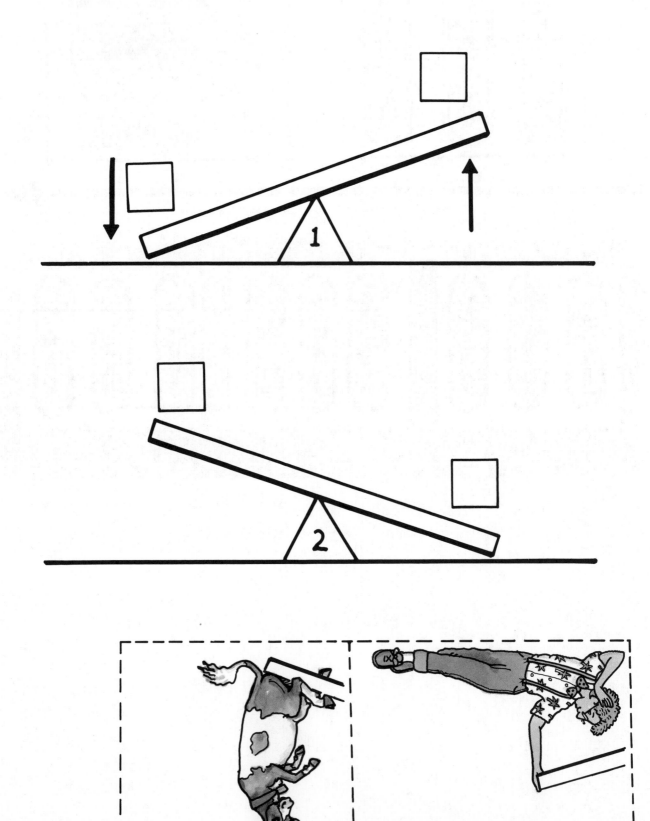

D.

Why did you say _____, Bleep?

Sunday

_____

Monday

_____

Tuesday

_____

Wednesday

_____

Thursday

_____

Blurpday

_____

Saturday

_____

A.

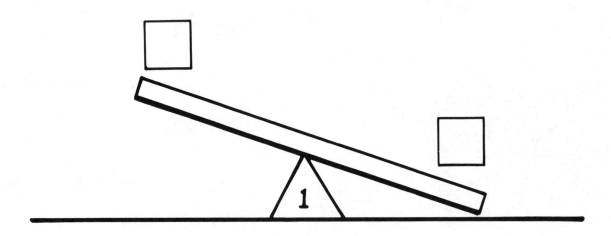

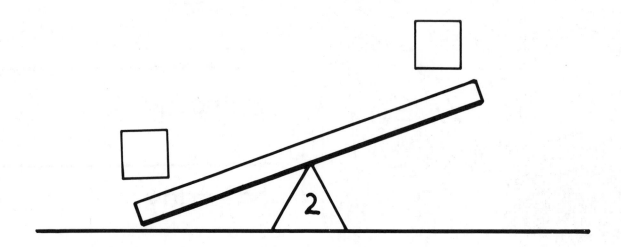

B.

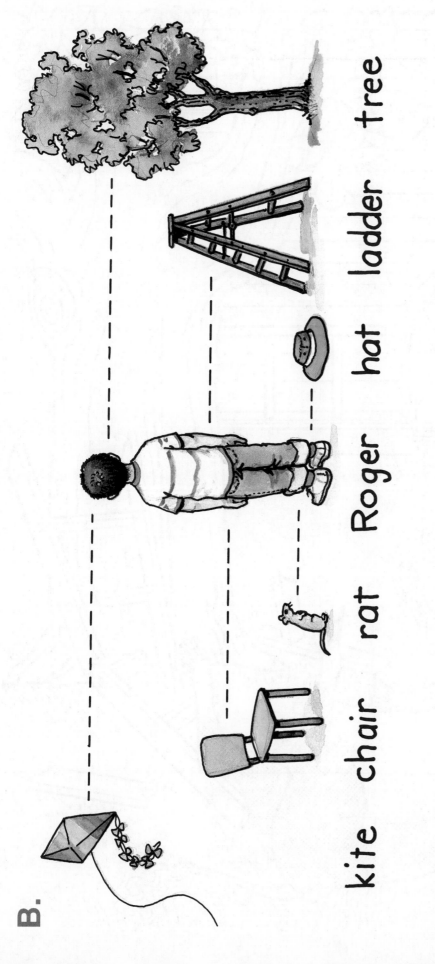

kite   chair   rat   Roger   hat   ladder   tree

1. Roger went to the <u>tree</u>. So he went

2. Roger went to the <u>rat</u>. So he went

3.

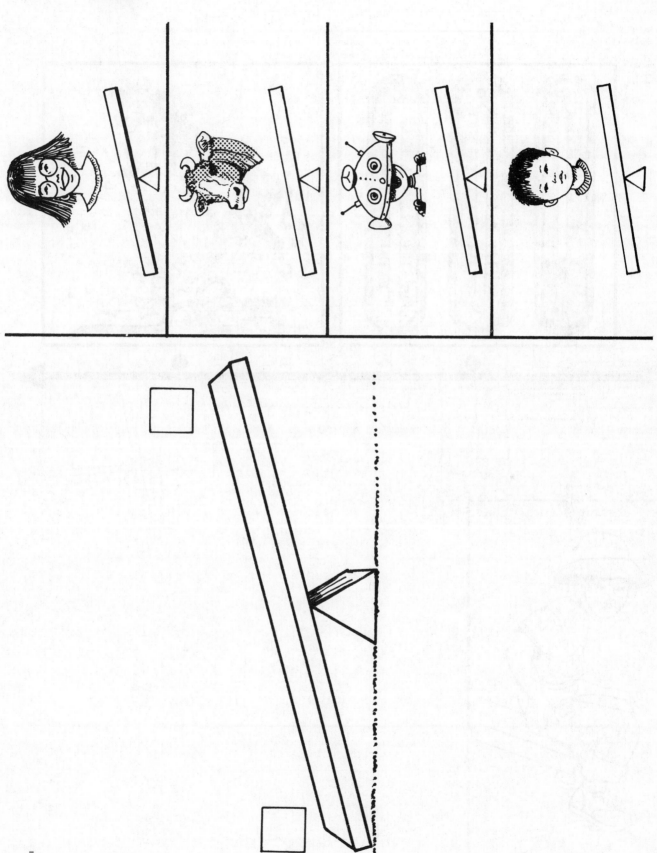

A.

B.

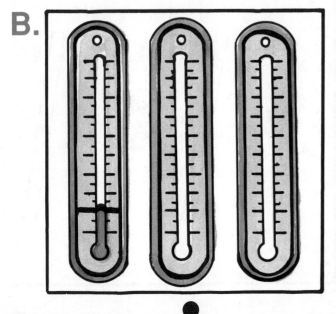

C.

bush Honey mouse Sweetie flower basket birdbath

1. Sweetie went to the <u>bush</u>. So he went

2. Sweetie went to the <u>flower</u>. So he went

3.

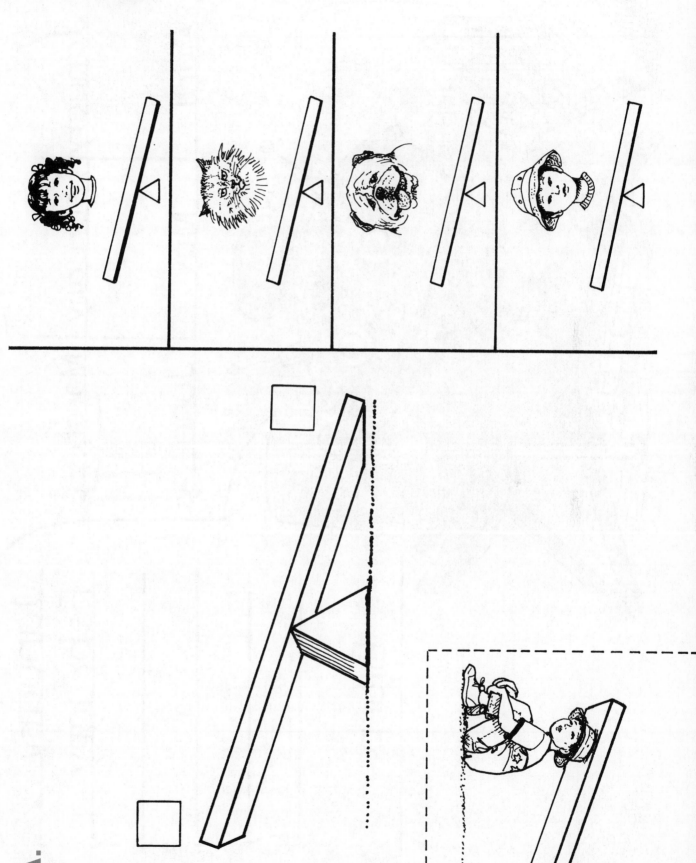

A.

B.

January | February | March

April | May | June

January
February
_____
_____
_____
_____
_____

Blurp.

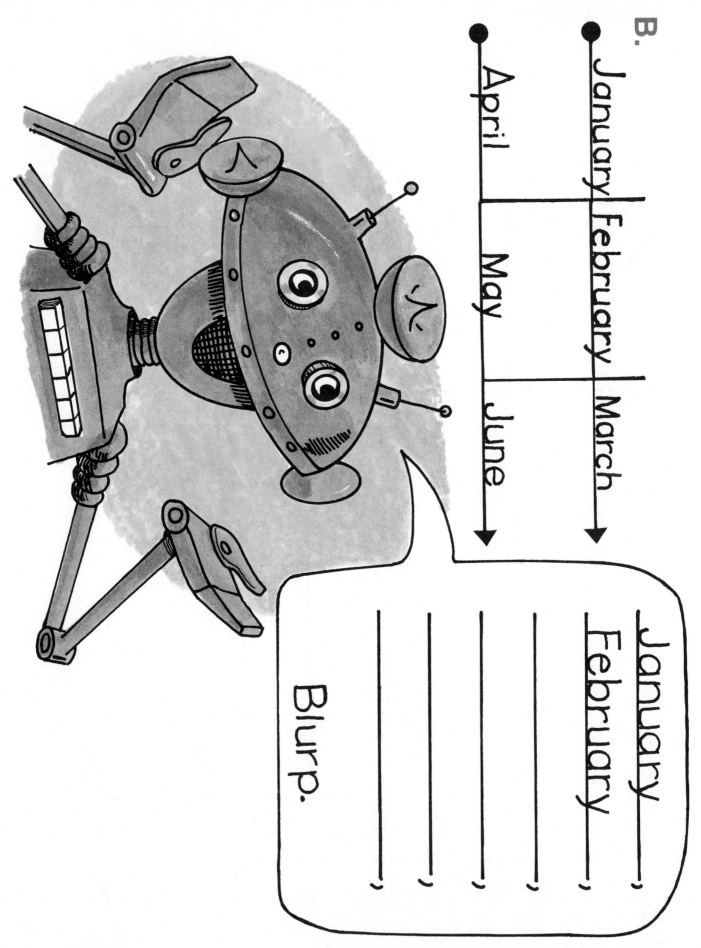

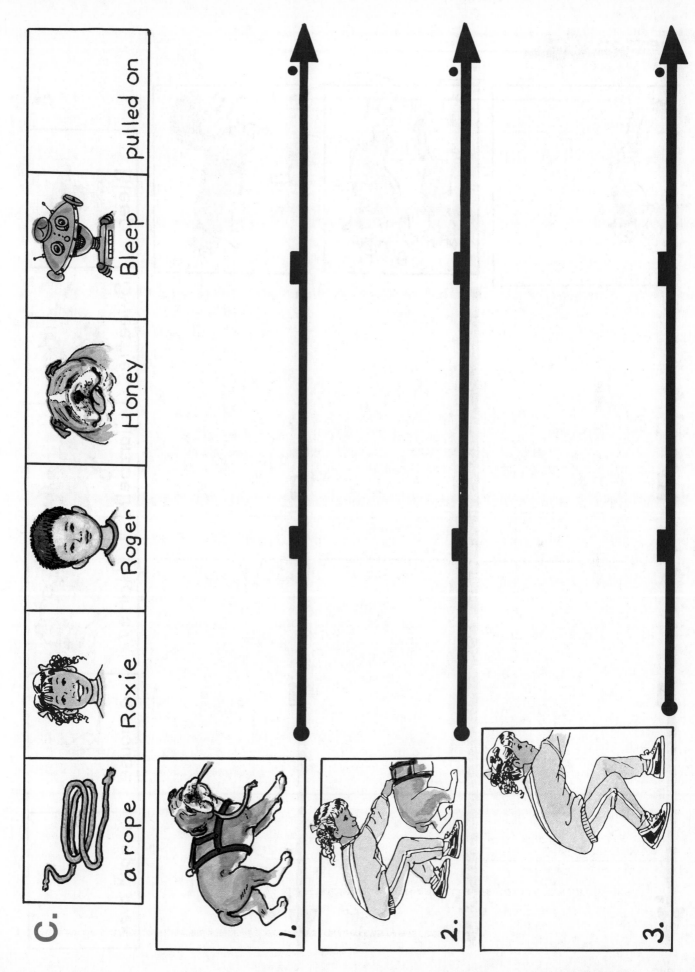

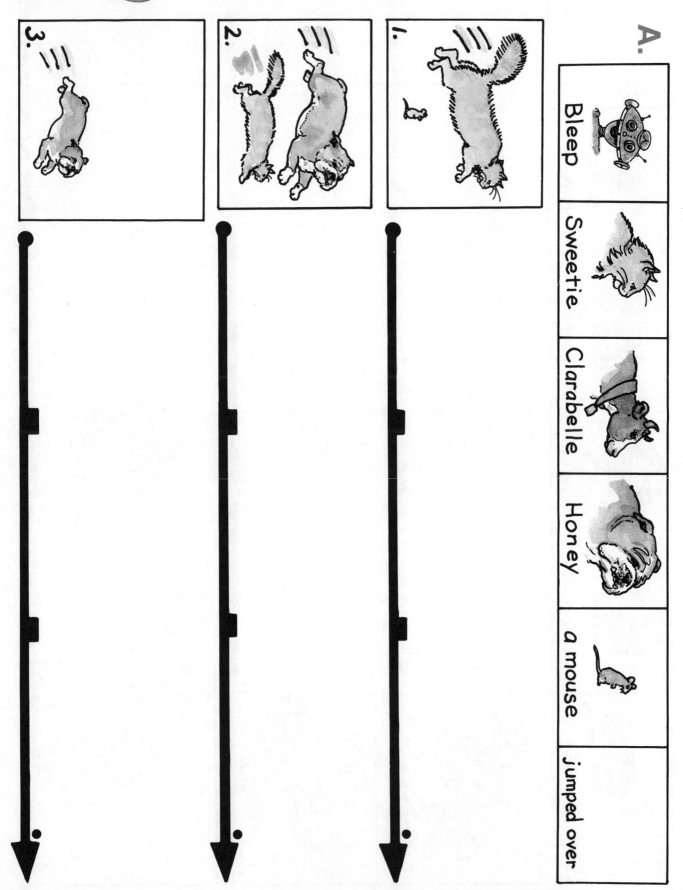

A.

Bleep | Sweetie | Clarabelle | Honey | a mouse | jumped over

1.
2.
3.

B.

September		

March	June	February	May
November	January	April	July
October	August	December	

C.

Lesson 66

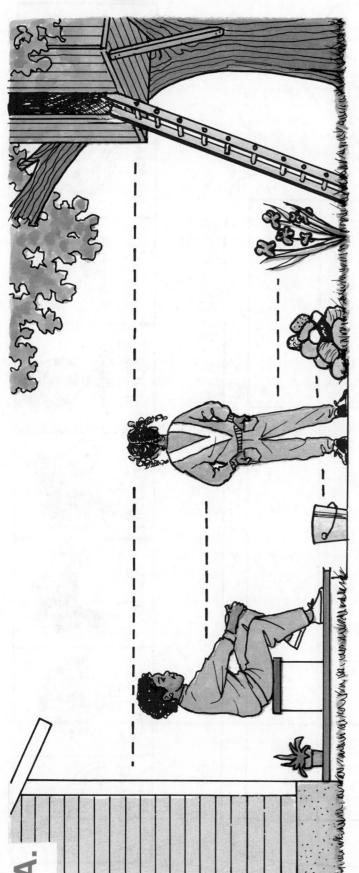

A.

her house her mother her pail   rocks flowers her treehouse

1. Roxie went to the rocks. So she went

2. Roxie went to her mother. So she went

3.

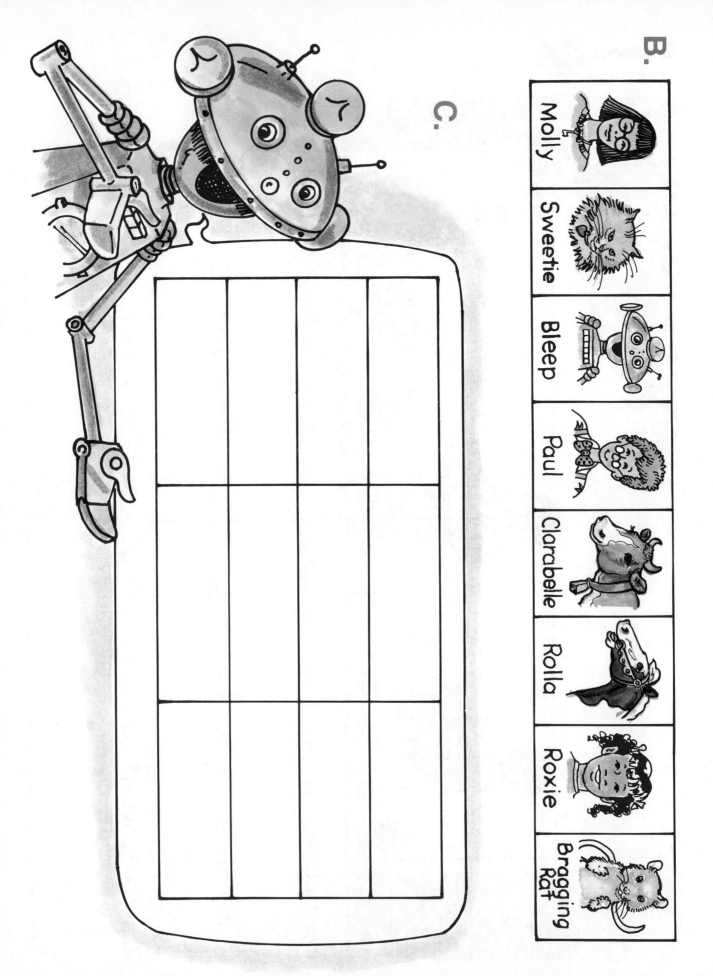

Molly	Sweetie	Bleep	Paul	Clarabelle	Rolla	Roxie	Bragging Rat

C.

Lesson 67

A.

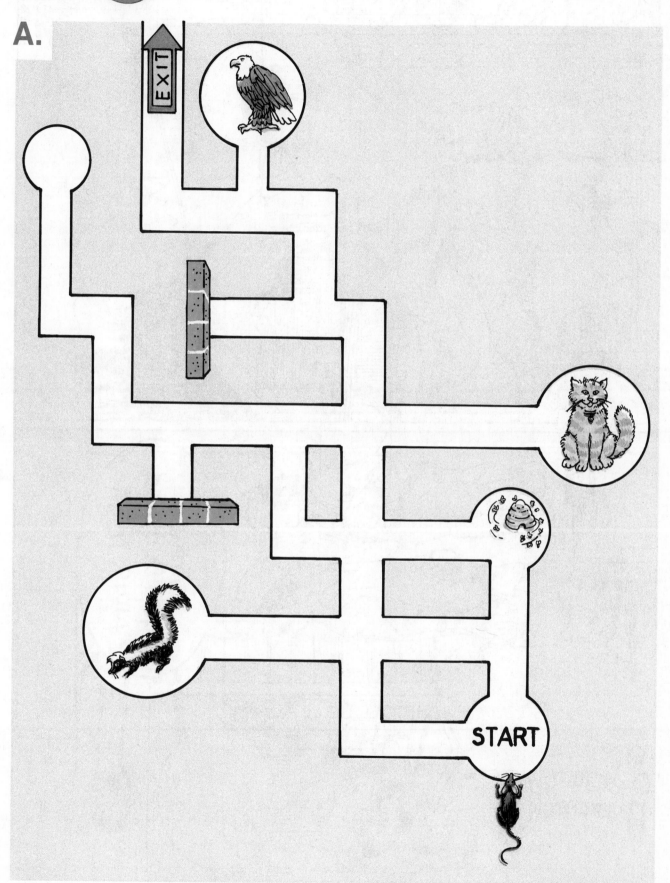

Lesson 68

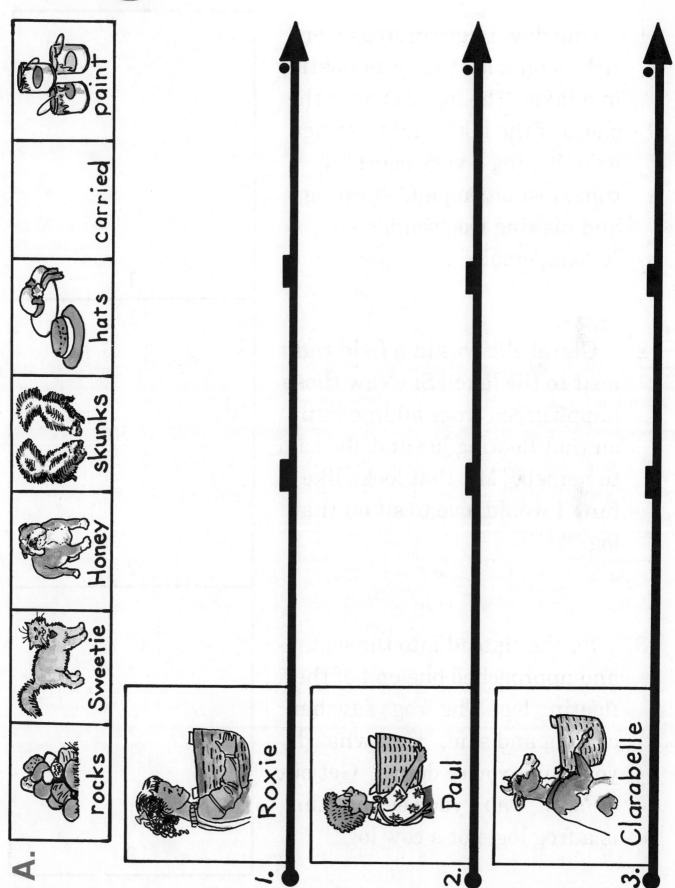

A.

rocks	Sweetie	Honey	skunks	hats	carried	paint

1. Roxie

2. Paul

3. Clarabelle

B.

1.   One day, 16 green frogs were sitting on a log that was floating in a lake. The log was near the shore of the lake, and the frogs were having a very peaceful time, just sitting and sunning and making frog sounds – "Croak, croak."

2.   Clarabelle was in a field right next to the lake. She saw those happy green frogs all lined up on that floating log and she said to herself, "My, that looks like fun. I would love to sit on that log."

3.   So she tiptoed into the water and approached one end of the floating log. The frogs saw her coming and said, "Hey, what do you think you're doing? Get out of here. Can't you see that this is a frog log, not a cow log?"

1
2
3

4.   But when Clarabelle _____

_____

_____

_____

_____

_____

_____

4

A.

Clarabelle	sat on	a hat	Sweetie
Paul	kissed	Molly	a rock
Bleep	painted	a pie	a rat

1. _____

2. _____

3. _____

B.

1. _____

     a.   true   false

     b.   true   false

     c.   true   false

2. _____

     a.   true   false

     b.   true   false

     c.   true   false

3. _____

     a.   true   false

     b.   true   false

     c.   true   false

4. _____

     a.   true   false

     b.   true   false

     c.   true   false

Roger

Clarabelle

Molly

Paul

Sweetie

Bragging Rat

C.

1.   Roger had many favorite hats. But his most favorite was a big black hat. One day, he put on that hat and went out for a walk. The day was very hot and Roger started to sweat.

2.   Roger didn't want to sweat all over his very favorite hat. So he took off his hat and put it under a bench that was next to a house. Roger planned to finish his walk without his hat, come back to the bench, pick up his black hat and go back home.

3.   What Roger didn't know was that the bench was next to Paul's house and that Paul planned to paint that bench pink. Roger also didn't know that when Paul painted things, he plopped paint on things that were nearby.

1

2

3

4.   So, while Roger was on his walk, Paul came out and

_____

_____

_____

_____

_____

_____

_____

_____

4

number 1	 kite	 honey	 turtle	wrecking yard

a. _____

b. _____

c. _____

d. _____

e. _____

 1. Bragging Rat	 2. Roger	 3. Bleep	 4. Sweetie	 5. Honey

f. _____

g. _____

h. _____

i. _____

j. _____

A.

☐ Paul

☐ Sweetie

☐ Rolla

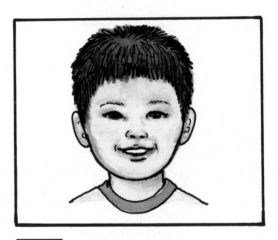

☐ Roger

☐ Honey

☐ Roxie

☐ Bleep and Molly

☐ Clarabelle

☐ Bragging Rats

Animals

 bird

 butterfly

 cat

 dog

 elephant

 fish

 rabbit

 snake

 spider

 turtle

Buildings

 barn

 church

 house

 movie theater

 school

 store

Clothing

 coat

 dress

 hat

 mitten

 pants

 shirt

 shoe

 sock